This igloo book belongs to:

...........................................

# igloobooks

Published in 2023
First published in the UK by Igloo Books Ltd
An imprint of Igloo Books Ltd
Cottage Farm, NN6 0BJ, UK
Owned by Bonnier Books
Sveavägen 56, Stockholm, Sweden
www.igloobooks.com

0823 001
2 4 6 8 10 9 7 5 3 1
ISBN 978-1-80108-558-8

Written by Stephanie Moss
Illustrated by Rayanne Vieira

Designed by Bethany Dowling
Edited by James Phoenix

Printed and manufactured in China

# Light up my HEART

igloobooks

Sprinkle some joy when you walk down the street
to light up the journeys of all that you meet.

Make someone smile
when it's cloudy and grey.

A small act of kindness will brighten their day.

The sweetest surprises
should taste really great.

Show that you love them
with treats you create!

Make someone laugh when it's all going wrong.

A dance...

... or a joke...

... even burst into song!

Two little words can mean more than you know.

So, tell someone thank you to make your love show.

When someone is struggling to cope on their own,
help them to feel that they're never alone.

Whatever you treasure,
it's kinder to share.

Enjoy it with loved ones
to show them you care.

We should all celebrate
just being GREAT!

The best gift of all
is your kindness.
It's free!

So, make sure it's there
for the whole world to see.

Kisses and cuddles are
one place to start.

But LOVE is the best way to
LIGHT UP YOUR HEART.